Write Your Best Story EVER! Notebook

Written by **Christopher Edge**

Illustrated by **Nathan Reed**

OXFORD
UNIVERSITY PRESS

OXFORD
UNIVERSITY PRESS

Oxford University Press is a department of the University of Oxford.
It furthers the University's objective of excellence in research, scholarship,
and education by publishing worldwide. Oxford is a registered trade mark of
Oxford University Press in the UK and in certain other countries

British Library Cataloguing in Publication Data

Data available

ISBN: 978-0-19-837782-5

1 3 5 7 9 10 8 6 4 2

Printed in China

Paper used in the production of this book is a natural,
recyclable product made from wood grown in sustainable forests.
The manufacturing process conforms to the environmental
regulations of the country of origin.

CONTENTS

HOW TO USE THIS BOOK

This book is filled with everything you need to write your **best story ever**. From **inspiration** and **tips** to the space to **plan** and **write** your story, you'll find everything you need inside.

★ Work through the book from cover to cover and by the time you get to the end you'll have written a story from **start** to **finish!** You'll find spaces to plan your story and try out different techniques, and pages for you to continue **writing** your own story as you work your way through the book.

★ You can also use the book to collect any **sparks of inspiration** – from newspaper cuttings to photographs – and keep them safe inside.

WORD WEBS

★ Use the word webs to help you find the right words for your story – from **action verbs** to **vocabulary** that is out of this world. If you can't find the word you're looking for, take a peek in a **dictionary** or **thesaurus** – use the word web as a starting point to spin your own creative vocabulary.

Word web

A particular style or type of story is called a **genre**. Choose the genre of story you would like to write from the **word webs** on these pages.

Remember, you could choose more than one genre for your story – how about writing a **historical mystery** or even a **scary romance?**

scary
GOTHIC
screenplay
school
SCIENCE FICTION
GHOST
fairy tale
sports
animal
DIARY
DETECTIVE
autobiography
CRIME

10

Author says . . .

Red herrings are false clues — try to plant some in your story to fool the detective and the reader too.

AUTHOR SAYS

★ If you're stuck, listen out for some **tips** from Christopher Edge, an award-winning children's author.

RED ALERT

★ Need some help with your **spelling, grammar** and **punctuation?** Red alerts give you hints on what you need to know to make your story the best ever.

RED ALERT!

When you are writing dialogue in your story, you need to remember to:

• put speech marks around' the words spoken

• use single (' ') or double (" ") quotation marks but keep them consistent

• start a new paragraph whenever the speaker changes

• only include the exact words the speaker says inside the speech marks

• put punctuation marks inside the speech marks

• give the name of the person speaking when this would make it clearer for the reader.

INSPIRATION STATION

The right word can give the reader more information about a character or situation.

Dr Dandiffer is an ethnobotanist. His speciality is the medicinal use of tropical plants. — **TIME STOPS FOR NO MOUSE** by Michael Hoeye

Quite a hullabaloo was breaking out upstairs, and most of the sounds were by no means pleasant. — **THE WEIRDSTONE OF BRISINGAMEN** by Alan Garner

INSPIRATION STATION

★ Take a leaf out of some of the best books around and find **inspiration** from the words of some fantastic children's authors. Try out the **techniques** they use in your own story.

GOT IT COVERED

★ Think about the story you want to tell. Can you write a blurb to sum this up? What kind of cover would you give your story?

★ Think about how you can create an **amazing picture** that will wow your readers and make them want to pick up your storybook.

★ Think about the **style of letters** you could use to write the **title** of your story. How about choosing gothic letters for a creepy mystery or a 3D eye-popping font for a science fiction story?

★ Remember you're the **author**. Don't forget to include your name on the cover!

The title of this story is:

_____

The **author** of this story is:

_____

The **blurb** for this story is:

_____

_____

_____

_____

_____

_____

_____

_____

Use this space to design the front cover for your story.

STORY SPARKS

Stuck for a story idea? Use one of these sparks of inspiration to set your imagination on fire!

NEWSPAPER HEADLINES:

★ Fill in the story you could write based on this **headline**. Or find your own newspaper headline that you think would make a great story and write it down here.

ROMAN SOLDIERS MARCH ON BRITAIN'S MOST HAUNTED MOTORWAY

OVERHEARD CONVERSATIONS

★ Who's **talking** below and what might this story be about? Write down your own ideas for a conversation to inspire a story.

So I told him if he wanted to be a vampire he had to eat his greens first . . .

PLACES YOU VISIT OR SEE ON TV

★ From crumbling castles to alien worlds, write down your ideas for **places** that would make a great story **setting**.

Chirp!

PEOPLE

★ A person you meet or glimpse on the street might give you the idea for a **character**. This might be a **mysterious stranger** or even your own best friend. What's their story? Write down your ideas for one or two characters.

ASKING QUESTIONS:

★ What if my mum could **read my mind?** How could a kitten beat a grizzly bear in a fight? Write down your own questions that could lead to an interesting story.

scary

GOTHIC

screenplay

school

SCIENCE FICTION

GHOST

fairy tale

sports

animal

DIARY

DETECTIVE

autobiography

CRIME

A particular style or type of story is called a **genre**. Choose the genre of story you would like to write from the **word webs** on these pages.

Remember, you could choose more than one genre for your story — how about writing a **historical mystery** or even a **scary romance**?

_____
_____
_____
_____
_____
_____
_____
_____
_____
_____
_____
_____
_____
_____
_____
_____

Write down any ideas you have for this story. These might be a word or phrase that catches your eye, an image that pops into your mind or just a random thought.

Connect the different **ideas**, **characters** and **places** to help you to create an original story.

Word web

adventure

mystery

comic book

FABLE

horror

SPY

script

comedy

historical

myth

PLAY

fantasy

ROMANCE

mash-up

THRILLER

Author says . . .

Give yourself time to daydream. Sometimes ideas for stories pop into your head when you're staring out of the window.

What stories could the following lines inspire?

Today is the one day in the year when all visitors are banned, on pain of death.
— *STRAVAGANZA: CITY OF MASKS* by Mary Hoffman

By and by there was to be heard a sound at once the most musical and the most melancholy in the world: the mermaids calling to the moon. — *THE ADVENTURES OF PETER PAN* by J. M. Barrie

You can get story ideas from the books you read too. Write down your ideas for a story you could tell from the **opening lines** of stories you have read.

_____

Every story is about someone or something. **A noun** names a person or a thing. Look at the different types of noun you could include in your story.

• A **proper noun** identifies a particular person, place or thing. Proper nouns begin with capital letters. James, Africa, Friday

• A **common noun** refers to people or things in general. dog, treasure, bridge

• A **concrete noun** refers to people and things that can be seen, touched, smelled, heard or tasted. pencil, banana, rain, beach, tune

• An **abstract noun** refers to ideas, qualities and conditions – things that cannot be seen or touched. danger, happiness, friendship

CREATING CHARACTERS

GREAT STORIES ARE ABOUT GREAT CHARACTERS.

Fill in the character profiles for the **hero** and villain in your story.

★ Remember your main characters don't have to be heroes or villains or even a person, but use these **character profiles** to collect your ideas about your leading characters.

Hero

The hero's name is:

_____

Do they have any **distinguishing features?**
The hero looks like:

_____
_____

How does your hero **speak?** What do they **say?**
The hero speaks like:

_____
_____

What is their **goal?** What do they want?
The hero wants:

_____
_____

What do they **do?** How do they get their goal?
The hero acts like:

_____
_____

Do others like them, laugh at them or feel scared?
Other people think the hero is:

_____
_____

Villain

The villain's name is:

_____

Do they have any **distinguishing features?**
The villain looks like:

_____

_____

How does your villain **speak?** What do they **say?**
The villain speaks like:

_____

_____

What is their **goal?** What do they want?
The villain wants:

_____

_____

What do they **do?** How do they get their goal?
The villain acts like:

_____

_____

Do others like them, laugh at them or feel scared?
Other people think the villain is:

_____

_____

Author says . . .

Think about the strengths and weaknesses you give each character. Does your hero have a secret phobia of spiders? Is your villain close to their gran?

INSPIRATION STATION

Descriptive details can give the reader an instant impression of a character.

Chudleigh Pomeroy came storming in, his toupee askew and his round face red with indignation.
— **MORTAL ENGINES by Philip Reeve**

Malfoy gave Professor Lupin an insolent stare, which took in the patches on his robes and the dilapidated suitcase.
— **HARRY POTTER AND THE PRISONER OF AZKABAN by J. K. Rowling**

SALLOW   **sunburned**

sinewy

drab   PUNY   smart

slender

brawny

bony   UNSHAVEN   **athletic**

svelte   **short**

PASTY

fine-boned

ROTUND

FAT   slight   **bloated**

scarred   **stocky**   CHIC

heart-shaped   WIRY

lanky   wrinkled

Which words from the **word webs** on these pages could you use to describe the hero in your story? Try to transform these into sentences and add your own ideas.

Hero

Which words from the **word webs** on these pages could you use to describe the villain in your story? Try to transform these into sentences and add your own ideas.

Villain

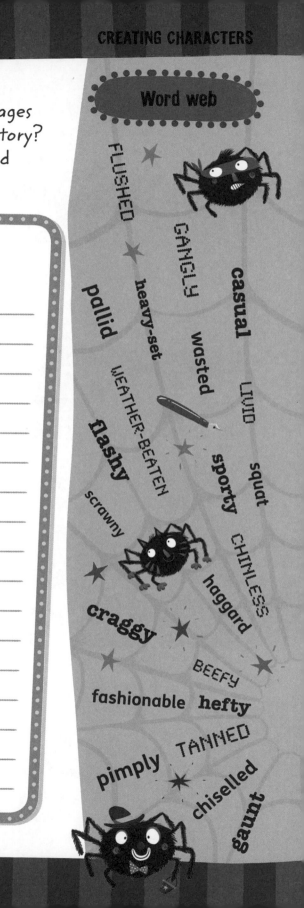

Word web

FLUSHED

GANGLY

heavy-set

wasted

pallid

WEATHER-BEATEN

casual

LIVID

squat

sporty

CHINLESS

flashy

scrawny

haggard

craggy

BEEFY

fashionable **hefty**

pimply TANNED

chiselled

gaunt

★ The **names** you choose can give your readers **clues** about your **characters**.

★ How would you expect a character called **Queen Tippsy-Wippsy** to behave?

★ What do you think an alien called **Glob** would look like?

Fill in a character profile for the other characters in your story.

CHARACTER NAME: _____

What words would you use to describe this character? What do they look like? What do they do?

_____
_____
_____

CHARACTER NAME: _____

What words would you use to describe this character: What do they look like? What do they do?

_____
_____
_____

CHARACTER NAME: _____

What words would you use to describe this character: What do they look like? What do they do?

_____
_____
_____

CHARACTER NAME: _____

What words would you use to describe this character:
What do they look like? What do they do?

_____

_____

_____

_____

CHARACTER NAME: _____

What words would you use to describe this character:
What do they look like? What do they do?

_____

_____

_____

_____

CHARACTER NAME: _____

What words would you use to describe this character:
What do they look like? What do they do?

_____

_____

_____

_____

RED ALERT!

An **adjective** gives more information about a noun. You can use adjectives to give more information about all the characters in your story.
The little, green alien zapped the frightened schoolboy.

• The adjectives **little** and **green** give more information about the alien and the adjective **frightened** gives more information about the schoolboy.

• Remember an adjective usually goes **before** the noun.

19

SETTING THE SCENE

Note down any **locations** that you want to include in your story.

W here does your story take **place**? When does your story happen? Whether you're writing a spy thriller or a fantasy adventure, a science fiction saga or a furry animal tale, the **setting** you choose will influence the story you tell.

REAL LIFE

★ If your story takes place in a **real-life location**, why not take a visit to this place?

★ **Sights, sounds, smells** and **sensations** can all help a reader to picture a place.

Note down any details you could use to describe these locations.

FANTASY

★ If you decide to set your story in a place you've **made up**, note down your ideas about this **location**. From lost mountains to cloud cities, look at images from films, comic books and videogames to help you picture these places.

Author says . . .

You can also use online maps and tools to explore anywhere in the world. If your story is set in New York, take a virtual walk down the streets of the Big Apple to spot things to make your setting seem real.

★ Your location might be a **town** like the one you live in or a **fantasy land** filled with legendary locations.

★ Mapping out the journey that your main character will follow in your story can give you ideas for **exciting new scenes**.

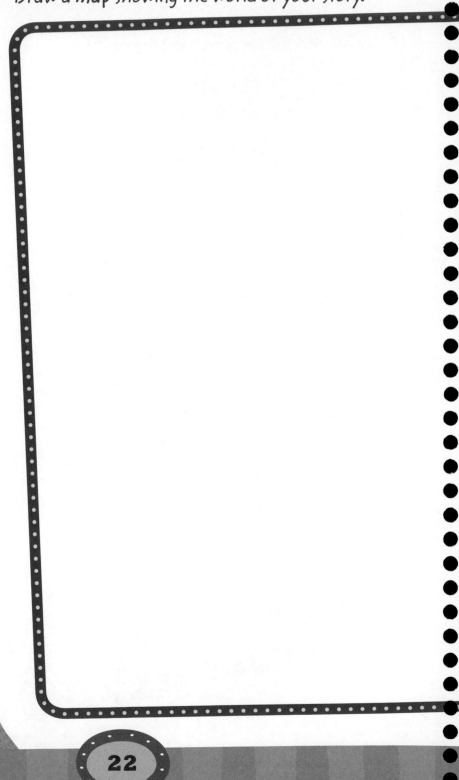

Draw a **map** showing the world of your story.

RED ALERT!

A **preposition** shows how things are related. It can describe the position of something, the time when something happens, or the way in which something is done.

*The water cascaded **over** the lip of the basin and dropped, in a miniature Niagara Falls, **onto** the kitchen floor. — MEASLE AND THE SLITHERGHOUL by Ian Ogilvy*

• The prepositions **over** and **onto** show exactly how the water spills from the basin to the floor.

• Here are some more prepositions you can use to help your readers picture the settings you describe: above, against, behind, below, beside, between, in, inside, near, on, off, outside, through, under

bush
SUN-DRENCHED
desert
moor
dyke
rainforest
RIDGE
crevice
island
cavern
hillock
WOODED
barren
LEDGE
fen
COVE
riverbank
INLET
DELL
grassland
MOUNTAIN
wasteland
GLACIER
ravine
beach
glen

You could use some words from the **word webs** on these pages to help you choose the different locations you could use in your story.

_____

_____

_____

_____

_____

_____

_____

_____

_____

_____

_____

_____

_____

_____

_____

_____

_____

_____

_____

_____

_____

Word web

bog
lagoon
KNOLL
wetland
prairie
forest
crevasse
MARSH
SAVANNAH
peninsula
steppe
SWAMP
BRAE
tundra
FELL
gorge
crag
dune
ESCARPMENT
HILL
hummock
gully
plateau

Author says . . .

Remember you're writing a story not a travel guide! Look for ways you can weave in details into the action, such as, 'His fingers scrabbled to find a grip on the crumbling rockface as the assassin took aim again . . . .'

WHAT'S THE PLOT?

You might have a head full of ideas, but you need to **organize** them into a **plot**. A plot is the things that happen in your story, arranged in a **logical** order.

★ A story needs a **beginning**, a **middle** and an **end**. Think about the event that kicks off your story and where you want your characters to be at the close of play.

Plan your beginning:

Plan your middle:

Plan your end:

★ Creating a **plot** is like climbing a mountain – each event or step in your story should **build** on the one before. There could be **twists** and **turns** as the characters face problems or challenges and peaks of excitement as dramatic events take place.

EXCITEMENT

START   FINISH

Plan out the plot of your story in the story mountain.

The hero discovers . . .

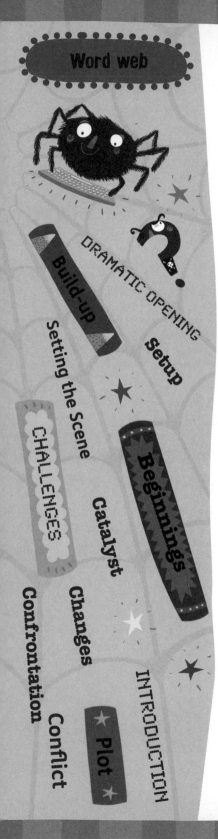

Word web

You could use the words in the **word webs** on these pages to help you to think about the **structure** of your story. Note down on the cards your ideas for different **scenes**.

Scene 1.

_____

_____

_____

Scene 2.

_____

_____

_____

Scene 3.

_____

_____

_____

Scene 4.

_____

_____

_____

Scene 5.

_____

_____

_____

Scene 6.

_____

_____

_____

Scene 7.

_____

_____

_____

Scene 8.

_____

_____

_____

Word web

STORY

MIX-UPS

Mistaken identity

Turning point

Action

Embarrassing situations

Endings

RESOLUTION

Close

Climax

Conclusion

CRISIS

Untangling

Problems

Author says . . .

What happens next? What would my characters do now? How will they get out of this situation? Working out the answers to these kinds of questions can help if you get stuck.

Think creatively — sometimes the weirdest idea can give you the right solution.

Maybe introducing a new character could give you the answer.

Visualize the **plot** of your story before you start writing it. Use this **flow chart** to show how different events link together.

Beginning

End

Or how about using a **chart** to plot the action of your story — every spike in the chart could show an event that sends the **excitement** levels soaring. Try to make the spikes taller as your story reaches its climax. The chart on page 27 might help you to make a start.

E

X

C

I

T

E

M

E

N

T

★   START   FINISH

A **conjunction** links clauses, words or phrases. You can use **conjunctions** to help you to think about the structure of your story. Link ideas and events together to make sure your plot makes sense.

• A **coordinating conjunction** joins clauses, and other phrases or words that are of the same importance in the sentence. *Lucy thinks the Prime Minister has been kidnapped and tries to rescue him.*

• **Coordinating conjunctions** include: and, but, or, nor, yet

• A **subordinating conjunction** introduces a subordinate clause, which is not as important as the main clause. *The kidnappers chase Lucy because they think she's the Prime Minister's daughter.*

• **Subordinating conjunctions** include: after, although, as, because, before, for, if, since, so, unless, when, whereas, whether, whilst, though, till, until

STORYTELLING

Who is going to tell your story? Whose **voice** do you want the reader to hear?

★ You might choose to write from the point of view of one of the characters using the words 'I' and 'we'. Using **a first person narrator** can make your story feel very real and exciting. Your readers can share the character's **thoughts** and **feelings**.

CHARACTER 1

When I saw her I thought . . .

Try telling the same story from the viewpoints of two different characters. This can be a good way to tell a love story!

CHARACTER 2

At first I didn't notice him . . .

★ Have a go at writing in the **first person** to bring these different characters to life. Think about the words your character would use to bring the story to life through their eyes.

A BOGEY

I am lurking inside the crustiest nose in the world . . .

A WISECRACKING DETECTIVE

I should've known this case was trouble when he walked into my office . . .

A DARING ASTRONAUT

I feel myself floating, weightless in space . . .

excited eager KIND fresh

HURTFUL obnoxious SMART

gentle foolish

brave ANNOYED

sad silly

RESENTFUL cautious

bold

If you choose to tell the story in the first person, think about the tone of voice you want to give your narrator.

You could make your narrator grumpy and mysterious or cheerful and silly.

_____

_____

_____

_____

_____

_____

_____

_____

_____

_____

_____

_____

_____

_____

_____

_____

You could choose words from the **word webs** on these pages to try out different **narrative** voices for the main character in your story.

Which one do you think works best?

_____
_____
_____
_____
_____
_____
_____
_____
_____
_____
_____
_____
_____
_____
_____
_____
_____
_____

Word web

grumpy

courageous

scared   moody

romantic

QUIZZICAL   JOLLY   SERIOUS

dreary   dull

cheerful   embarrassed

secretive

sinister   clever   mysterious   INTELLIGENT

CALM   smug

sarcastic   IRRITATED

angry   SYMPATHETIC

★ If you don't want to tell the story from the point of view of one of the characters, you can write in the **third person**, using the words 'he', 'she', 'it' and 'they' instead.

★ If your story has lots of characters and you want to show their different points of view, writing in the **third person** can let the reader see the story from **different angles**.

★ You can move between the minds of different characters to show their **thoughts** and **feelings** or just describe the thoughts of one character from a third person viewpoint.

Have a go at using the **third person** to describe your main character. Think about them walking into a room and how you describe this. Remember to use **he, she, it** or **they** instead of **I** or **we**.

_____

_____

_____

_____

_____

_____

_____

_____

_____

_____

_____

Author says . . .

Whether you choose to tell the story in the first person or the third person, remember to stick to this.

If you switch back-and-forth between different viewpoints you'll leave your readers' heads spinning!

The **tense** of a verb tells you when the action of the verb takes place. You can choose to write your story in the past or present tense.

• The **present tense** is used to describe something that is happening now. It is usually shown by having no ending, or by adding **–s**.
Bilbo climbs the mountain.

The dwarves are happy.

The dragon sniffs the air.

• Using the **present tense** can make the reader feel as though they're watching the action of the story as it happens.

• The **past tense** is used to describe something that happened earlier. The past tense is usually shown by adding **–ed**.
Bilbo climbed the mountain.

The dragon sniffed the air.

• Watch out for verbs which change completely in the past tense.
is ——→ was
go ——→ went
think ——→ thought

STARTING YOUR STORY

Write down your **different ideas** for the event that could kick-start your story.

A good story should **grab** your reader's attention from the very **first line**. This doesn't mean you have to start your story with a huge explosion – although you can if you want to!

My story starts with . . .

My story starts with . . .

★ A **mystery** might begin with a dead body being discovered, whilst if you're writing a **funny story** you want to start with an **event** that will leave your reader in stitches. Whatever type of story you want to tell, try to set the **right tone** from the very start.

My story starts with . . .

Author says . . .

Which idea do you think is the best? However you choose to start your story, make sure this event kick-starts the plot. Get the reader asking questions and keep them turning the pages to find out what happens next.

My story starts with . . .

My story starts with . . .

Fantastic opening lines hook the reader from the very start.

It was a dark, blustery afternoon in spring, and the city of London was chasing a small mining town across the dried-out bed of the old North Sea. — **MORTAL ENGINES by Philip Reeve**

The first thing you find out when yer dog learns to talk is that dogs don't got nothing much to say. — **THE KNIFE OF NEVER LETTING GO by Patrick Ness**

If you are interested in stories with happy endings, you would be better off reading some other book. — **THE BAD BEGINNING: A SERIES OF UNFORTUNATE EVENTS by Lemony Snicket**

- There are lots of different ways of starting a story.
- Have a go at using these **different techniques** to write your opening lines.

DESCRIPTION

★ Introduce the characters and the setting of your story.

ACTION

★ Throw your readers into the middle of an exciting event.

DIALOGUE

★ Let the reader hear the characters' voices.

AN INTRIGUING QUESTION OR STATEMENT

★ You could start with something like 'Beware of the mouse – that's what the sign on the gate said.'

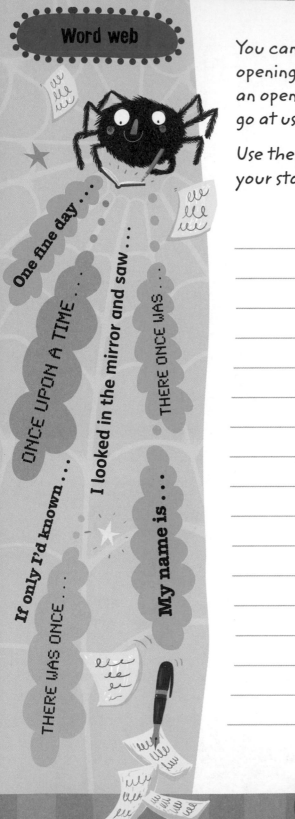

Word web

One fine day . . .

ONCE UPON A TIME . . . .

I looked in the mirror and saw . . . .

THERE ONCE WAS . . . .

If only I'd known . . . .

My name is . . . .

THERE WAS ONCE . . . .

You can also **change** or **twist** traditional story openings to surprise the reader. You could choose an opening line from the **word webs** and have a go at using this to start your story.

Use these pages to continue writing the start of your story.

Word web

IF I HADN'T BEEN . . .

There was . . .

I WOKE UP AND . . .

It started like a normal day . . .

Once there was . . .

IT WAS A . . .

One day . . .

I didn't want to go to . . .

RED ALERT!

Remember to use **paragraphs** to make your story easy to read and understand.

Start a new paragraph in your story when you are going to start writing about something different such as a different person, location or event.

BUILD-UP

Imagine you're **directing a film** as you write each scene of your story. Think about how you could move the **camera** around to help the reader to picture the **scene**.

★ You could **describe** a crowd of thousands in a single line and then switch to a **close-up** to describe a tear rolling down the face of your hero.

• Fill in the storyboard to plan the build-up of your story. These are the scenes that follow on from the opening of your story.

• What happens next?

• What does your main character do?

1.

4.

7.

2.

_____

_____

3.

_____

_____

5.

_____

_____

6.

_____

_____

8.

_____

_____

9.

_____

_____

dulcet HARMONIOUS raucous ACRID tinny foul SWEET mellifluous harsh melodious JARRING grating harsh shrill piercing RASPING THIN ACRID succulent bitter HOT disgusting bland FIERY unappetising revolting

A **picture** can paint a thousand words, but if you choose the **right words** you can help your readers to imagine a cast of a thousand characters and visualize places they've never seen before.

You could use the words in the **word webs** to help you to bring the scenes from your **storyboard** to life, as you continue with your story here.

_____
_____
_____
_____
_____
_____
_____
_____
_____
_____
_____
_____
_____
_____
_____

Word web

DELICIOUS
zesty
nauseating
INSIPID
mild
rancid
burnt
juicy
mouth-watering
fruity
sweet
HOT
mellow
fresh
ACIDIC
METALLIC
mild
nutty
pungent
PEPPERY
SPICY
sour
salty
SAVOURY
smoky
sugary
sharp

Word web

WHIFFY
stinky
rotten
FETID
foul
odorous
foul-smelling
reeking
EVIL-SMELLING
pongy
SWEET-SMELLING
stinking
smelly
MUSTY
fragrant
AROMATIC
perfumed
SCENTED
sweet

You could use more words from the **word webs** on these pages to bring the scenes from your storyboard to life, as you continue your story here.

Word web

WOOLLY
WATERY
velvety
fine
grainy
bristly
fluffy
feathery
dry
COARSE
knobbly
creamy
crinkly
moist
PAPERY
rough
rubbery
STIFF
runny
spongy
SOFT
smooth
silky
stringy
STICKY
crunchy
SPRINGY
lumpy
squashy
fibrous

You can use **metaphors** and similes to help you to describe things in interesting and unusual ways. Think about how you can use similes in your story as you continue writing here.

Similes can focus the reader on specific details that the writer wants them to imagine.
The building looked like a fiery ghost, with great bursts of flame coming from the windows.
— *A SERIES OF UNFORTUNATE EVENTS* by Lemony Snicket

'A bad idea, Professor Lockhart,' said Snape, gliding over like a large and malevolent bat.
— *HARRY POTTER AND THE CHAMBER OF SECRETS* by J. K. Rowling

At last with a glorious swoop like the dive of a wild sea-bird, the witch and her broomstick came down on the Hurricane Mountains. — *GOBBOLINO THE WITCH'S CAT* by Ursula Moray Williams

What would a
moon-skulled
person look like?

How would someone
who walked like
a huge awkward
chicken move?

PROBLEMS AND CHALLENGES

What **problems** and **challenges** will the main character encounter in the next part of your story?

Use the boxes below to help you to plan the twists and turns of the plot.

PROBLEM

★ What is stopping your main character from carrying on with the **action** of your story?

CHALLENGE

★ What **obstacle** does your main character need to overcome now to move the plot of the story forward?

SITUATION

★ What **difficult position** might your main character find themselves in and how will they get out of this?

DIFFICULTY

★ Think about the **key problem** your main character is facing and how they will **resolve** this.

COMPLICATION

★ What could happen to make the situation your main character is in even **more complicated**?

CONFLICT

★ Who might be trying to **stop** your hero from achieving their goal?

CONFRONTATION

★ What fights, arguments or **difficult encounters** could your main character face?

Now that you have planned the next part of your story, carry on writing it here. Remember to think about how the **main character** will respond to each of the **obstacles** they face.

_____

_____

_____

_____

_____

_____

_____

_____

_____

_____

_____

_____

_____

_____

_____

_____

_____

If your hero is drugged with a poison, how will they escape from this situation?

As you write, think about how the problems or challenges will change your main character.

ACTION!

If your story has fight scenes, car chases and **huge explosions**, getting the action right will make your reader feel like they're watching a blockbuster movie.

Author says . . .

Every action scene you include should move the plot of your story forward. Don't just include a fight to give your characters something to do!

★ Before you start to write an action scene, you could use the **storyboard** to plan out exactly what's going to happen. This will help you to describe the action in a realistic way.

★ Don't try to describe every punch or kick – including a few specific details can help the reader to **imagine** what is happening.

Use the storyboard to plan your action.

1.

2.

3.

4.

5.

6.

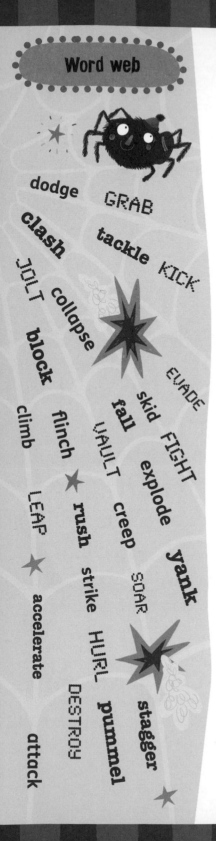

Word web

dodge GRAB
clash tackle KICK
JOLT collapse
block EVADE
climb flinch skid FIGHT
fall VAULT explode yank
LEAP rush strike creep SOAR
accelerate HURL pummel stagger
attack DESTROY

Carry on writing your story here. As you write your scenes, think about which **verbs** you could use to help the reader picture the action. Remember to use the **past** or **present tense** form of the verb, depending on how you've chosen to tell your story.

_____
_____
_____
_____
_____
_____
_____

RED ALERT!

- Some **verbs** identify an action:
  The goat **attacked** the troll.

- Other **verbs** identify thoughts and feelings:
  The troll **wondered** why the goat was picking on him.

- Many verbs can be either **active** or **passive**. With an **active verb**, the subject is often who or what does something.
  The troll **cleans** his cave every week.

- With a **passive verb**, the focus is on what happens, rather than who does something.
  The troll's cave **is cleaned** every week.

- Using **active verbs** can help you to make your story more dynamic.

Word web

CHARGE
LIMP sidestep
fly CHASE
crouch
catch
hurtle
cut
steal
LUNGE
dash
crash
collide
DIVE
punch
shoot
drop
swoop grip prod
trip PULL
turn
SPIN
WRESTLE zap

For every action there should be a reaction. Show your readers the impact of the actions you describe.

The next thing Alex knew, the heel of Wolf's palm had rammed into his chest, pushing him back with astonishing force.
— STORMBREAKER by Anthony Horowitz

Just as the creature lunged forwards to kill him, Hiccup was grabbed around the ankle by one of Stoick's hairy hands, and pulled back through the hole he had climbed in. **— HOW TO BE A PIRATE by Cressida Cowell**

It can be exciting to watch a car chase on the cinema screen, but reading pages and pages describing the same car chase will quickly send the reader to sleep.

Keep your **action scenes** short for maximum impact, as you carry on with your story here.

Try to **avoid** any action clichés like your hero walking away from an exploding building without a scratch.

Include details that **appeal** to the reader's senses to help them imagine the experience:

the heat of the blast

the sound of tearing metal

the unstoppable force of the shockwave

ZOOOOM!

TALK THE TALK

Think about what you want the characters in your story to say. You can use **dialogue** to:

★ move the **plot** of your story **forwards** – perhaps you could drop a clue to a mystery into a conversation;

I'LL BE BACK

★ **reveal** something about the characters in your story – what a character says and how they say it can show what they think and how they are feeling.

RED ALERT!

When you are writing dialogue in your story, you need to remember to:

• put speech marks around' the words spoken

• use single (' ') or double (" ") quotation marks but keep them consistent

• start a new paragraph whenever the speaker changes

• only include the exact words the speaker says inside the speech marks

• put punctuation marks inside the speech marks

• give the name of the person speaking when this would make it clearer for the reader.

Look back at your story so far. Use this space to note down any changes you want to make to your dialogue.

INSPIRATION STATION

Adjectives and adverbs can be used to provide information about the way a character speaks.

'Stupid things!' Alice began in a loud, indignant voice. — **ALICE'S ADVENTURES IN WONDERLAND by Lewis Carroll**

'What's the matter?' asked Sorrel sarcastically, venturing so close to the edge of the chasm that her furry toes were over empty space. 'Don't you like mountains?' — **DRAGON RIDER by Cornelia Funke**

★ Remember people don't always say what they mean and the same should be true for the characters in your story too!

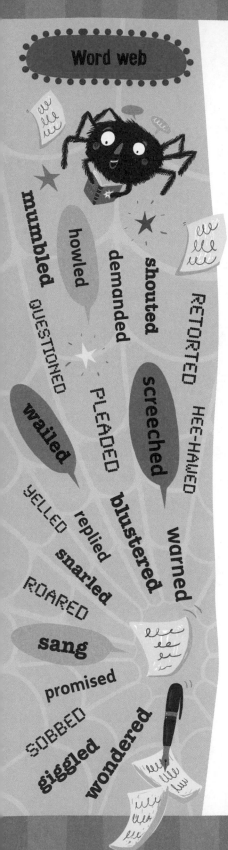

Word web

mumbled
howled
demanded
shouted
QUESTIONED
RETORTED
HEE-HAWED
wailed
PLEADED
screeched
warned
YELLED
replied
blustered
snarled
ROARED
sang
promised
SOBBED
giggled
wondered

Carry on writing your story here. Think about how different characters in your story **speak**. You could help the reader **recognize** who's talking by giving your villain an annoying catchphrase or making your heroine's friend always speak in a sarcastic tone.

Most of the time 'said' is the only **verb** you will need to describe who is speaking in your story. In some cases, the **speech verbs** in this **web** can be used to add something to your story!

Word web

ADMITTED
brayed
purred
sighed
agreed
whispered
miaowed
interrupted
hissed
ASKED
begged
muttered
barked
LAUGHED
argued
NAGGED
screamed
answered
threatened
tweeted
CHEEPED
WHIMPERED
bragged
cried
BELLOWED
whined
LIED

Author says . . .

Try to make the different characters in the story sound like individuals. Reread their dialogue, but cover up each character's name.

If you can't tell which character is speaking, you might need to change the dialogue.

CREATIVE VOCABULARY

The words you use can help your story come to life in the mind of the reader. Get **creative** with the **vocabulary** you choose to create characters, settings and scenes that they will never forget.

★ Try using your imagination to **build** your own words.

You could invent a new fear such as 'mathstestaphobia' or create a dinosaur known as the Ugliasaurus.

mathstestaphobia

phobia

phobia

phobia

phobia

You can also create new words by blending two words to create a **compound word**. Your 'sleep-fogged' hero might be 'terror-stricken' as he wakes to find a 'saliva-cobwebbed' spectre looming 'wraith-like' above him! Pick some more to blend your own compound words.

sleep + fogged = sleep-fogged

_____ + _____ = _____

_____ + _____ = _____

_____ + _____ = _____

INSPIRATION STATION

Chirp!

The right word can give the reader more information about a character or situation.

Dr Dandiffer is an ethnobotanist. His speciality is the medicinal use of tropical plants. — **TIME STOPS FOR NO MOUSE** by Michael Hoeye

Quite a hullabaloo was breaking out upstairs, and most of the sounds were by no means pleasant. — **THE WEIRDSTONE OF BRISINGAMEN** by Alan Garner

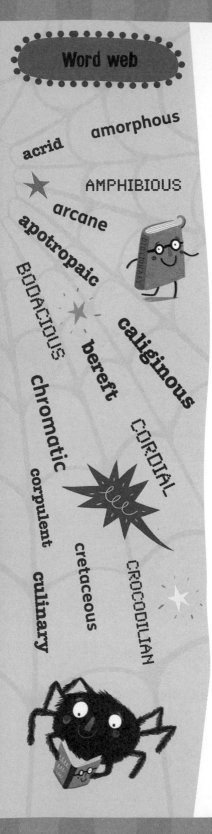

acrid

amorphous

AMPHIBIOUS

arcane

apotropaic

BODACIOUS

bereft

caliginous

chromatic

CORDIAL

corpulent

cretaceous

CROCODILIAN

culinary

Remember the words you use should always be the **right ones** for your story. If any of the words in the **word webs** on these pages help you to describe the characters and events in your story then use them, but don't choose a word just because it sounds impressive.

Word web

herbaceous

harrowing

fathomless

GILDED

disconsolate

DORMANT

dauntless

labyrinthine

ephemeral

HEWN

lachrymose

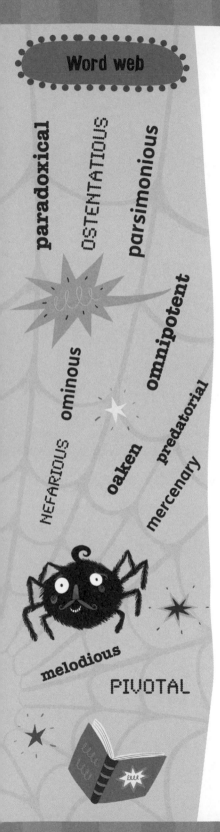

Word web

paradoxical
OSTENTATIOUS
parsimonious
omnipotent
ominous
NEFARIOUS
oaken
predatorial
mercenary
melodious
PIVOTAL

You can use more words from the words webs on these pages to make your writing more varied and interesting, as you carry on with your story here.

_____
_____
_____
_____
_____
_____
_____
_____
_____
_____
_____
_____
_____
_____
_____
_____
_____
_____
_____
_____

Word web

rancid

rapacious

pulchritudinous

RAMBUNCTIOUS

sumptuous

stentorian

TUMULTUOUS

sibilant

SONOROUS

turgid

unadorned

VULPINE

Author says . . .

Don't always use the first word that comes into your mind. Instead of saying that a character in your story talks a lot, why not describe them as 'loquacious' or call the person a 'blatherskite.'

You can find exciting vocabulary in lots of different places: blockbuster films, TV shows, songs, apps and video games.

Keep an ear to the ground to steal new words for your story.

THE END

Every **great story** needs a **great ending.** You want to wrap up the plot in a way that leaves the reader satisfied.

★ Whether it's your hero solving the mystery, finding lost treasure or triumphing in a final battle against a fire-breathing dragon, any problems or challenges you've introduced in your story should be **resolved** before you write 'The End'.

Plan the **end** of your story here.

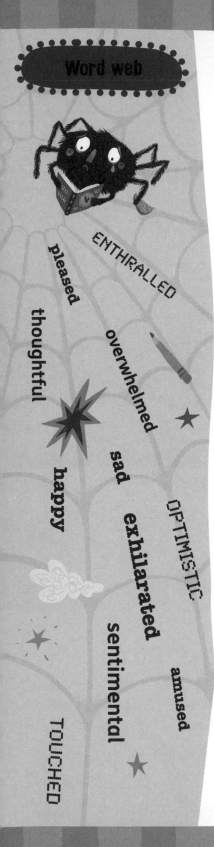

ENTHRALLED

pleased

thoughtful

overwhelmed

sad

happy

OPTIMISTIC

exhilarated

sentimental

amused

TOUCHED

What emotions do you want the reader to feel when they **finish the story?** You could use the words in the **word webs** to help you to think about the mood you want to create in your **closing scenes** here.

Word web

SCARED TO GO TO SLEEP

awed

EXCITED

surprised

inspired

scared

hopeful

NERVE-JANGLED

tense

Fantastic final lines stay with a reader long after they've put the story down.

I am haunted by humans. — **THE BOOK THIEF** by Markus Zusak

The scar had not pained Harry for nineteen years. All was well. — **HARRY POTTER AND THE DEATHLY HALLOWS** by J. K. Rowling

Light falls through the window, falls onto me, into me. Moments. All gathering towards this one. — **BEFORE I DIE** by Jenny Downham

HOME

Use these pages to finish your story. Try and end your story with a **fantastic final line.**

The ending could show how characters have been **changed** by the events of the story — a cowardly hobbit could now be a brave hero or a school bully turn into a best friend.

✻ The final line ✻

Author says . . .

A cliff-hanger ending can leave your readers in suspense, but this works best if you're planning to carry on the action in a follow-up story.

Remember you don't have to have a happy ending.

CHOOSING A TITLE

You shouldn't judge a book by its cover, but choosing the **right title** can encourage readers to pick up your story. The title could give the reader a **hint** about what the story will be about. It might tell them:

Use this space to plan your title.

TYPE OF STORY

★ What type of story is it – an **adventure**, a **romance**, a **mystery** or a **mash-up**?

CHARACTER OR SETTING

★ Your title could say something about the **main character** or **setting** – *Alice in Wonderland* tells you about both!

IDEAS AND EVENTS

★ Your title could say something about the ideas and events – *Stop in the Name of Pants!* lets you know that this is a story that has something to do with a pair of pants . . .

Think up some attention-grabbing titles that will make your story stand out.

Author says . . .

You could choose a one-word title like 'Vanished' or a long title like 'The Day I Swapped My Dad For Two Goldfish.'

The Day I Swapped My Dad For Two Goldfish

WRITING A TV OR FILM SCRIPT

Have a go at turning your story into a TV or film script. First of all, break your story down into **scenes** to help you to write your script. Every time you change to a new time or place, that's the signal to start a new scene.

Whether you want to make a science-fiction film or a TV detective show, you'll need to write a **script** to bring your **ideas to life**.

★ You have to set out your script in a special way. Don't include lots of description – only write what the audience will see and hear.

★ TV and films can use **special features** to tell a story, such as captions that tell the audience when and where a scene takes place.

3.

6.

1.

2.

4.

5.

7.

8.

versions

shot

cuts

dialogue

LOCATIONS

stage directions

edits

SCENES

description

acts

PLACE

action

SPECIAL EFFECTS

flash-forward

zoom in

cast

draft

voiceover

view

PANORAMA

split-screen

outdoor shoot

The three most important things you need to include in your script are:
- **Setting** — where and when each scene in your story takes place.
- **Dialogue** — what the characters in your story say.
- **Action** — what the characters in your story do or what happens to them.

Try to also use some of the other features from the **word webs** in your script.

Scene 1

Character name

Character name

Character name

Carry on with your **script** here.

Word web

time star

MOTION

credits

INDOOR SHOOT

flashback

TREATMENT

BREAK

actor screens

camera angle

BACKDROP

adaptation

aside

AD LIB

dissolve

characters

caption

STUNT

INSPIRATION STATION

In a script, characters' names are presented in capitals and stage directions placed between brackets.

'Ghost of the Future!' he exclaimed, 'I fear you more than any spectre I have seen.'
— A CHRISTMAS CAROL by Charles Dickens

SCROOGE: (shouting) Ghost of the Future, I fear you more than any spectre I have seen!
— SCRIPT VERSION

Whether it's an explosive finale to a blockbuster film or a cliff-hanger ending to a TV show, think about how you can keep your audience **entertained** to the very last line as you carry on with your script here.

★ Remember your script will need a **beginning**, a **middle** and an **end**.

WRITING A COMIC BOOK

When you create a **comic book**, the only budget you have is the limits of your imagination. From visits to strange alien planets to superheroes saving the world, comic books use **pictures** and **words** to bring any story to life.

KAZOOOOM!

Comic books use special features to tell a story, such as speech bubbles to show what the characters say and thought bubbles to show what they're thinking.

I am a speech bubble!

I am a thought bubble!

Have a go at turning your story into a **comic book** in the next few pages.

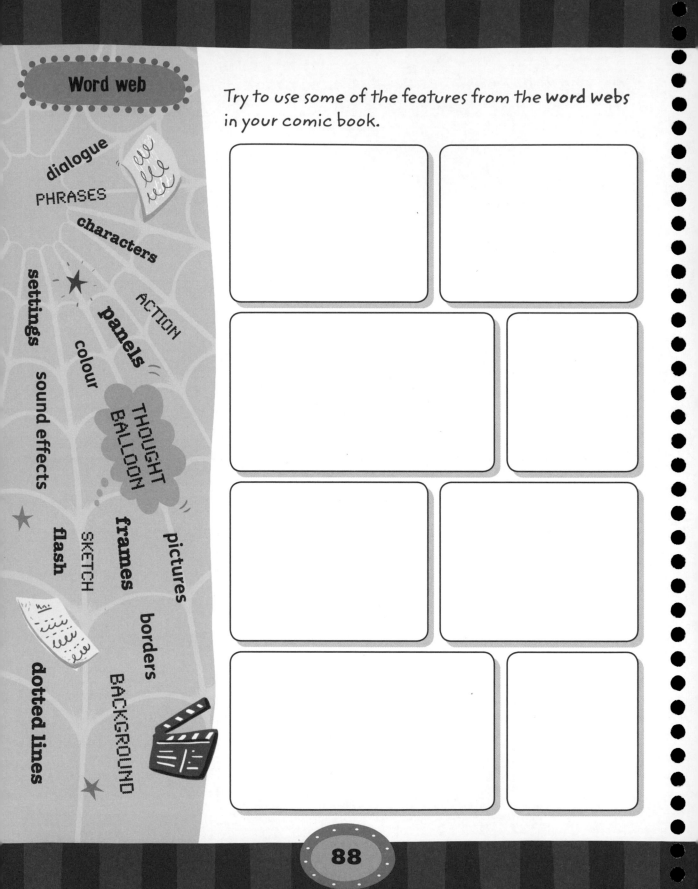

Word web

dialogue

PHRASES

characters

ACTION

panels

settings

colour

sound effects

THOUGHT BALLOON

flash

frames

SKETCH

pictures

dotted lines

borders

BACKGROUND

Try to use some of the features from the word webs in your comic book.

Remember to include your own **speech bubbles** and *thought bubbles* here.

Word web

GRAPHIC NOVEL

WORD BALLOON

scenes

SPLASH

cartoons

gutter

lettering

description

shadows

captions

design

GRAPHICS

comic strip

speech bubble

box

tier

spread

You may have to edit your story to make it fit your comic book template.

★RED ALERT!★

- **Synonyms** are words that mean the same or nearly the same as each other, such as **enormous** and **huge**, or **horrid** and **nasty**.

- Using **synonyms** can help you to avoid repeating the same words in your comic book.

- **Antonyms** are words that mean the opposite of each other, such as **quick** and **slow**. You can change the meaning of many words by adding a prefix such as **un-**, **im-** or **dis-** at the start of the word, such as **unhappy**, **impossible**, **disliked**, or changing the suffix at the end of the word, such as **careless** and **careful**.

- Using **antonyms** can help you to contrast different things in your story.

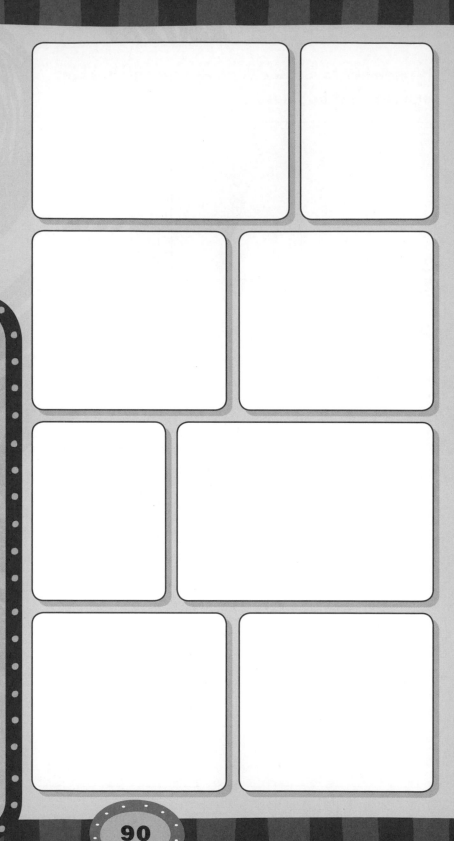

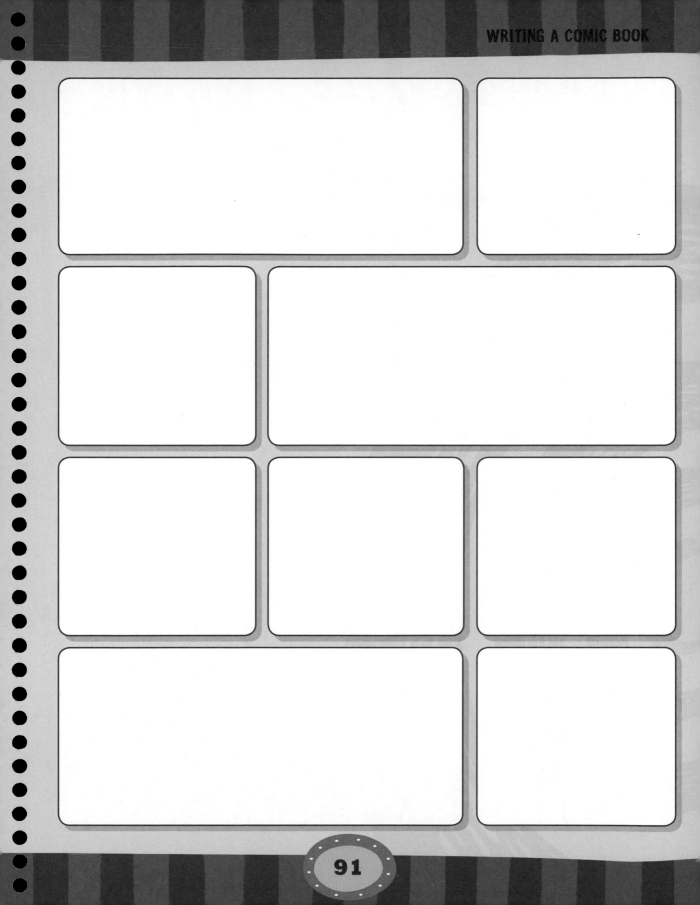

IS IT FINISHED?

So you think you've finished your story? Before you rush to put this book back on the shelf of your local bookshop, **first ask yourself questions on these pages.**

★ Have you designed your **cover** and written your **blurb**? Go back to pages 6 and 7 to check.

★ Does the **plot make sense?** Are there any **loose ends** you've forgotten to tie up?

★ Don't leave your heroine dangling off the edge of the cliff in one scene and then show her sipping a fruit juice on the beach in the next without explaining how she escaped from certain death!

Add any other questions here that you want to check.

☑ Do I have chapter headings?

☐

☐

☐

Word web

Do the characters in the story seem real?

Are there any scenes that don't move the plot forward?

DOES THE PACE OF THE STORY MOVE FAST ENOUGH TO KEEP THE READER'S INTEREST?

Can you tell which characters are speaking when you read their dialogue?

Does the opening of the story grab the reader's attention?

CAN YOU PICTURE THE SETTINGS DESCRIBED?

Check the **spelling** in your story to make sure you haven't mixed up any of these commonly confused words:

• **clothes** are things that you wear ——→ **cloths** are pieces of material you use to wipe a table

• **nether** means low down or lower ——→ **never** means not ever or not at all ——→ **neither** means not either

• **collage** is a picture made by sticking small objects to a surface ——→ **college** is a place where people go to learn after they have left school

• **exited** means someone has left a place ——→ **excited** means feeling eager or enthusiastic about something

You need to make sure that readers will be able understand every part of your story. Check that what you have written is **clear** and **accurate**, with full stops and capital letters in the correct places.

Use this space to make a note of any errors you know you tend to make in your writing. Make sure you check these.

Once you've made any **final revisions** to your story, why not show it to a friend to get a **second opinion**?

Sometimes a **fresh pair of eyes** can spot any mistakes you've missed.

Ask your friend to jot down any suggestions they have.

Choose a friend who likes the type of story you've written and ask if they can suggest any improvements you can make.

☐ Does the opening of the story grab your attention?

☐ Do you find any parts of the story confusing?

☐ Do the setting and characters work?

☐ Do you find the ending satisfying?

Author says . . .

Try to avoid clichés and clumsy phrases and don't be afraid to make changes. If in doubt, cut it out!

★RED★ ALERT!

• Check your spelling of words ending in **–ise** or **–ize**. Most of these can be spelled either way in English in the UK (organize, recognize, visualize), while some words can only be spelled with an **–ise** ending (surprise).

• You must choose one spelling and use it **consistently**.

The perfect reference companion for your notebook is

How to Write Your Best Story EVER!
Top tips and trade secrets from the Oxford word experts
Christopher Edge

Age 7+

(Paperback)

Also available:

Age 8+ — Oxford Primary Dictionary

Age 8+ — Oxford Primary Thesaurus

(Hardbacks)

Age 10+ — Oxford School Dictionary

Age 10+ — Oxford School Thesaurus

(Paperbacks)

Age 10+ — Oxford Mini School Dictionary

Age 10+ — Oxford Mini School Thesaurus

(Paperbacks)

Age 7+ — Oxford Primary Grammar, Punctuation and Spelling Dictionary

Age 10+ — Oxford School Spelling, Punctuation and Grammar Dictionary

(Paperbacks)

www.oxfordchildrens.co.uk/dictionaries